Pisces
Astrology Coloring Book

Color Your Zodiac Sign

The 12 Signs

Sign Symbols

ARIES

TAURUS

GEMINI

CANCER

LEO

VIRGO

LIBRA

SCORPIO

SAGITTARIUS

CAPRICORN

AQUARIUS

PISCES

Pisces

February 19 - March 20

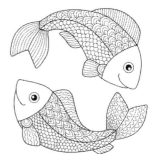

PISCES ARE FRIENDLY and compassionate people. Like all water signs they are extremely emotional empaths. Their ruling planet of Neptune makes them much more intuitive and artistic than other signs. They are known for their wisdom and non-judgmental behavior. Pisces are not materialistic and generally don't give money and material goods a second thought. They are the most tolerant of all the zodiac signs and have great gentleness. Because of these same qualities however they can be overly trusting and victims to those with bad intentions.

Symbol: Fish

Planet: Neptune

Element: Water

Colors: Purple, Violet, Green

Traits: Compassionate, Intuitive, Gentle, Fearful, Overly Trusting

Constellation:

PISCES

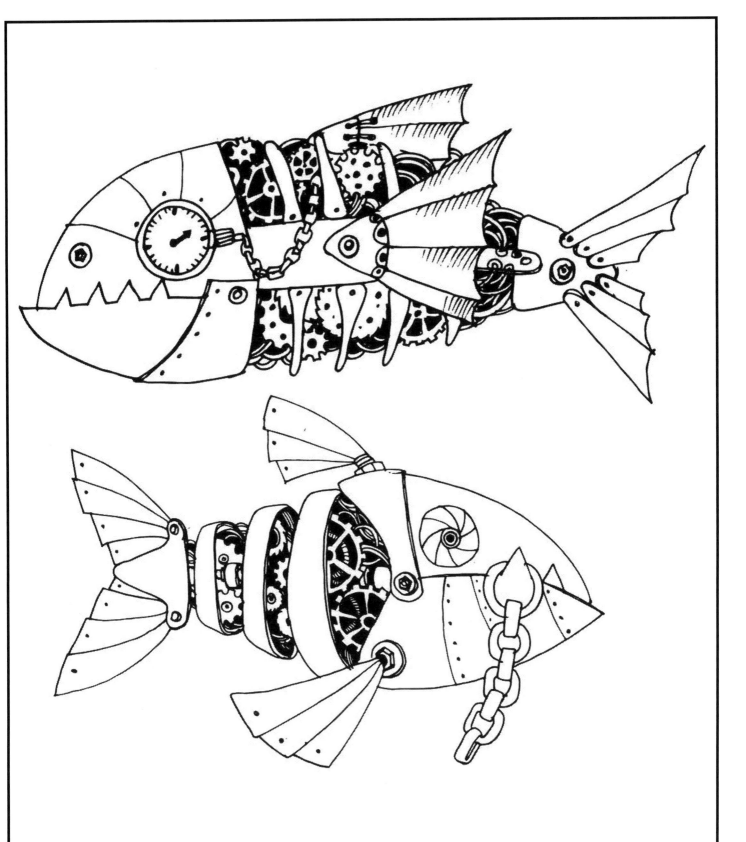

PisCes

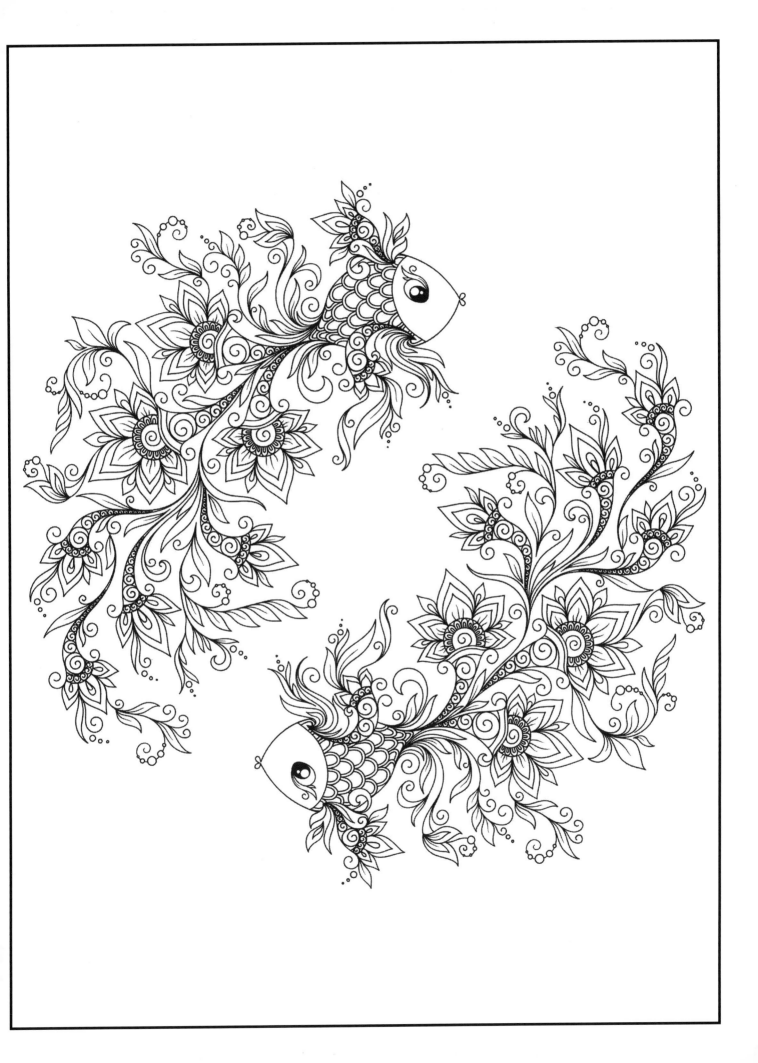

Pisces

Pisces

Pisces

PISCES

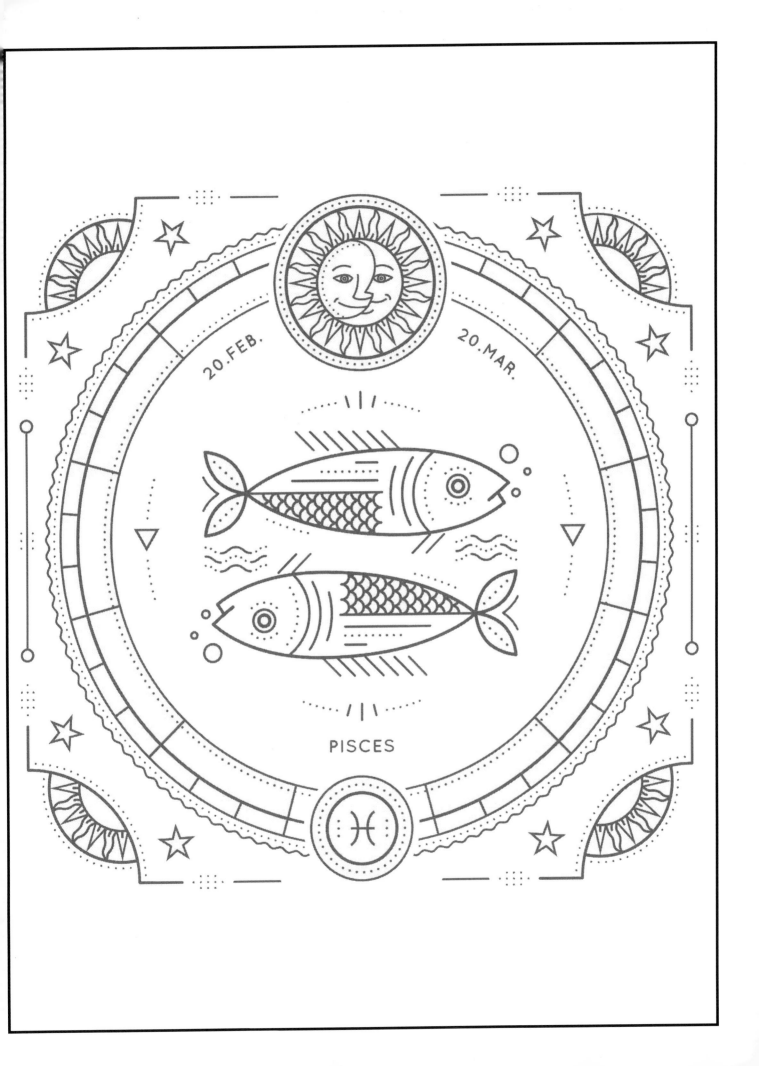

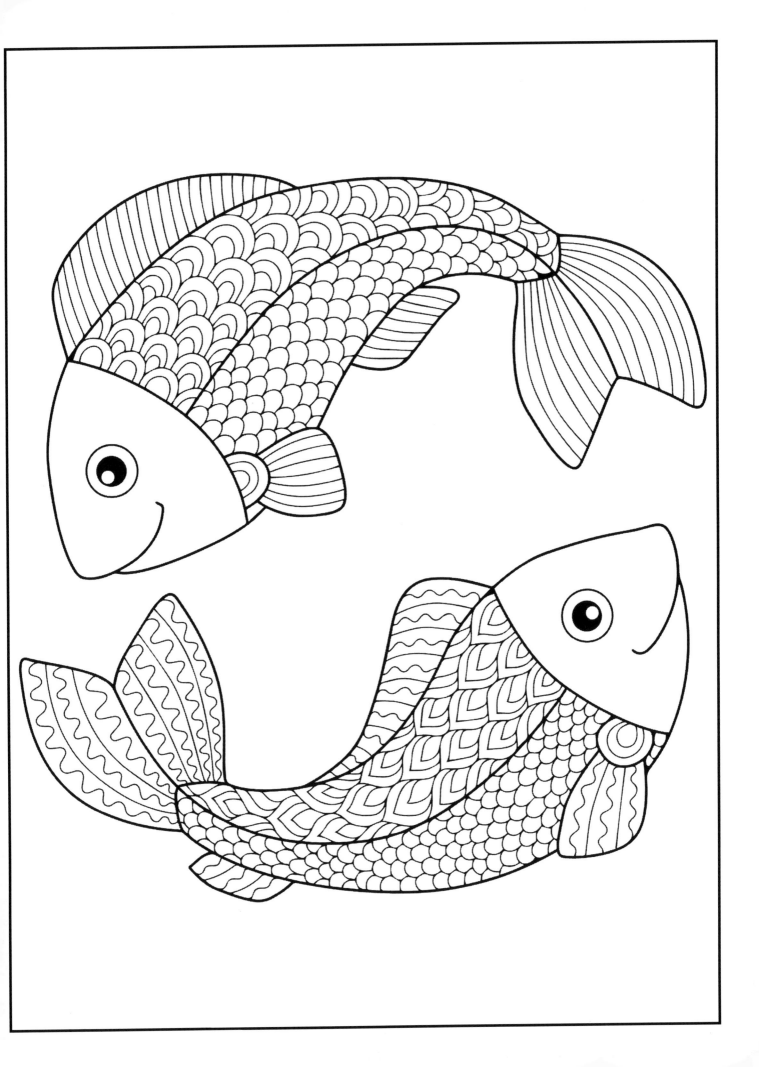

♓ *Pisces*

Made in the USA
Columbia, SC
16 December 2021

51704457R00041